THE ANDREW LLOYD WEBBER ANTHOLOGY

A REALLY USEFUL
GROUP PUBLICATION

Andrew Lloyd Webber

Andrew Lloyd Webber had his first piece of music published when he was nine. Now, not yet 40, he is the most successful British composer of musicals ever. He's written seven major hit musicals and he is the only composer to have had 3 shows running simultaneously in the West End and on Broadway. His name is in lights in most major capital cities around the world and more often than not his shows are the hottest ticket in town. The dazzle of his achievements can be blinding. This anthology shows its source: the tunes, the songs.

He has a talent rare in any area of music in any century: a gift for writing memorable melodies.

He had a fine grounding. Like many composers, Lloyd Webber grew up in a richly musical family. His father was a director of composition at the Royal College of Music – and subsequently Director at the London College of Music. His own compositions are now being re-recorded and released. "His father had this sense of melody and Andrew's inherited that, I'm sure", says his mother. She in her turn allowed her son the run of their flat to stage his earliest musical theatres and risked the wrath of neighbours as he played on one piano, her husband on another and Julian, his brother, attacked the cello.

He grew up in a home which seems to have been a hyperactive rehearsal room which was also a laboratory. When, in his mid teens, he met Tim Rice with whom he was to collaborate with such originality, he had already written 8 musicals.

Not only did he imbibe a classical musical education from his father, it was his father who brought the first rock'n'roll record into the house. One characteristic of Lloyd Webber's work has always been the ease and freshness with which he speaks different musical tongues: he is bi-lingual in classical and rock and can slip from one to the other with tremendous effect. He makes it fun. Wouldn't the 'Pie Jesu', he suggests, be marvellous sung by the Everly Brothers? "One can but dream".

A further element of course is his flair for and massive application to the details of musical theatre. It obsesses him: and the brilliant theatricality of the shows is proof of that relentless obsession.

Yet at the heart of the matter are the tunes. These fall into several groups of which the most striking are those which appeared at the time to be bold, even crazy and wholly unexpected. 'Jesus Christ Superstar' was a very high risk anthem when it was first suggested – blasphemous in those far off days. 'Don't Cry For Me Argentina' again, a song about a dictatrix in South America seemed as remote from the public taste as an interrogative pop song about the founder of the Christian religion: and as for 'Gus The Theatre Cat!' But again and again he stuck to his hunch, to his own musical genius and to the challenge of fine words which brought out the sinewy lyrical aspect of his talent.

He also has the ability to write music which is deeply moving 'I Don't Know How To Love Him', 'Memory', 'Pie Jesu', 'The Music Of The Night'. The melodies in themselves are touching and resonant. And where do you categorise 'Unexpected Song' – one of the best he has written in my opinion. He draws on many banks of musical experience.

This is a fair selection from 20 years' work. An indication of its richness is that 'Everything's All Right' (from 'Superstar') – a cunning and original piece – cannot find a place here. No doubt it will be included in the next anthology and no doubt there will be many more volumes to come. I have a feeling, to adapt Al Jolson, that "we ain't seen nothing yet".

Melvyn Bragg
18th September, 1987

JOSEPH AND THE AMAZING
TECHNICOLOR DREAMCOAT
ANY DREAM WILL DO 12
CLOSE EVERY DOOR 7

JESUS CHRIST SUPERSTAR
JESUS CHRIST SUPERSTAR 19
I DON'T KNOW HOW TO LOVE HIM 23
KING HEROD'S SONG 27

EVITA
DON'T CRY FOR ME ARGENTINA 42
ANOTHER SUITCASE IN
ANOTHER HALL 48
HIGH FLYING ADORED 52
RAINBOW HIGH 27

CATS
MEMORY 61
MR. MISTOFFELEES 66
GUS THE THEATRE CAT 69

SONG AND DANCE
UNEXPECTED SONG 82
TAKE THAT LOOK OFF YOUR FACE 86
TELL ME ON A SUNDAY 77
THE LAST MAN IN MY LIFE 90

REQUIEM
PIE JESU 97

STARLIGHT EXPRESS
STARLIGHT EXPRESS 108
ONLY YOU 112
MAKE UP MY HEART 114
THERE'S ME 105

THE PHANTOM OF THE OPERA
THE PHANTOM OF THE OPERA 136
ALL I ASK OF YOU 121
MUSIC OF THE NIGHT 126
WISHING YOU WERE SOMEHOW
HERE AGAIN 131

JOSEPH AND THE AMAZING TECHNICOLOR DREAMCOAT

Close Every Door

Music by Andrew Lloyd Webber
Lyrics by Tim Rice

laugh at me, Dark-en my day-time and tor-ture my per-son, De-stroy me com - plete-ly, then throw me a-

night.
way. If my life were im-port-ant I would ask will I

live or die, But I know the ans-wers lie far from this world.

Close ev-'ry door to me, keep those I love from me

To Coda ⊕

Child - ren of Is - rael are nev - er a - lone For I know I shall find my own peace of mind, For I have been pro - mised a land of my own.

9

(Choir) La la la la la la, la la la la la la, La la la la la la, la la la la la la,

La la la la la la, la la la la la la, La la la la la la, la.

Any Dream Will Do

Music by Andrew Lloyd Webber
Lyrics by Tim Rice

JESUS CHRIST SUPERSTAR

Jesus Christ Superstar

Music by Andrew Lloyd Webber
Lyrics by Tim Rice

why'd you choose such a back-ward time and such a strange land? _____
could Ma - hom - et move a moun-tain or was that just P. R? _____

If you'd come to - day you would have reached a whole na - tion,
Did you mean to die like that? Was that a mis - take _____ or

Is - rael in four B. C. had no mass com - mu - ni - ca - tion.)
did you know your mes - sy death would be a re - cord brea - ker?)

(Don't you get me

wrong)   (don't you get me wrong now)   (don't you get me
Don't you get me wrong, _   Don't you get me wrong _

Je - sus Christ, _ su - per - star, _ do you think you're what they say you are? _

Je - sus Christ, _ su - per - star, _ do you think you're what they say you are? _

Repeat to Fade

Je - sus Christ, _ su - per - star, _ do you think you're what they say you are? _

I Don't Know How To Love Him

Music by Andrew Lloyd Webber
Lyrics by Tim Rice

Slowly, tenderly and very expressively

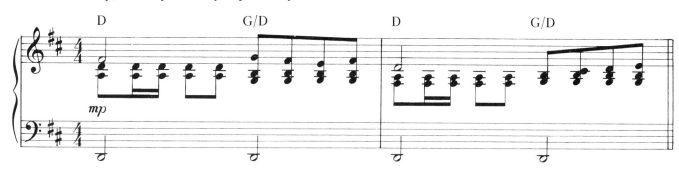

I don't know how to love _____ him What to do, how to move _____ him, I've been changed yes real - ly changed In these

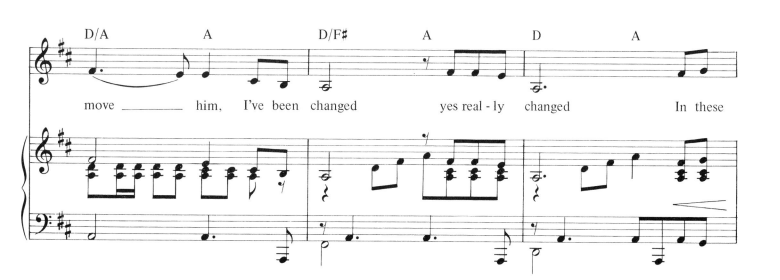

25

King Herod's Song

Music by Andrew Lloyd Webber
Lyrics by Tim Rice

Moderato, ad lib.

Je - sus I am o - ver - joyed to meet you face to face

You've been get - ting quite a name all a - round the place ___ Heal - ing crip - ples

rais - ing from the dead And now I un - der - stand you're God at least that's what you've

Je - sus you just won't be - lieve the hit you've made 'round here

You are all we talk a - bout, the won - der of the year___

Oh what a pi - ty if it's all a lie

Still I'm sure that you can rock the cyn - ics if you try.___

29

I on - ly ask things I'd ask an - y su - per - star

What is it that you have got that puts you where you are?___

I am wait - ing yes I'm a cap - tive fan I'm

31

EVITA

Rainbow High

Music by Andrew Lloyd Webber
Lyrics by Tim Rice

EVA

I don't real-ly think I need the rea-sons why I

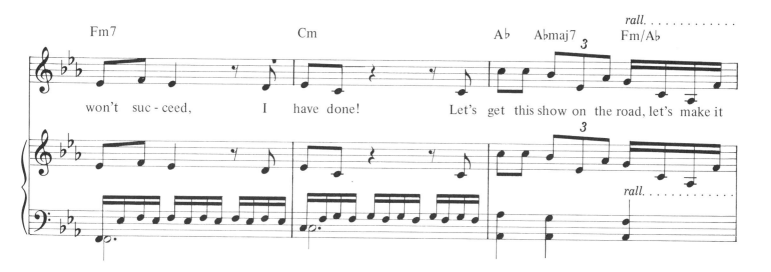

won't suc-ceed, I have done! Let's get this show on the road, let's make it

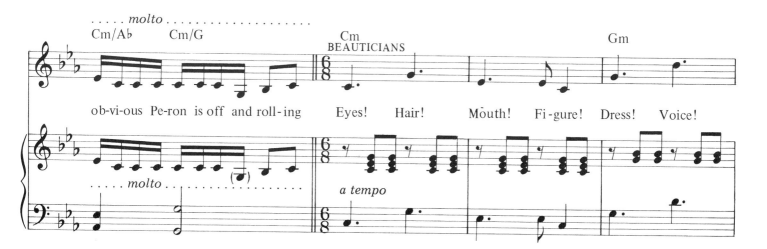

ob-vi-ous Pe-ron is off and roll-ing

BEAUTICIANS

Eyes! Hair! Mouth! Fi-gure! Dress! Voice!

Style! Move-ment! Hands! Ma - gic! Rings! Gla-mour! Face! Dia-monds! Ex -

cite-ment! Im-age!
(Solo) I came from the peo-ple pro-duct they need to a - dore me it's vi - tal you sell me So Christ-ian Di -
So Mach - i - a -

or me from my head to my toes: I need to be dazz-ling, I want to be
vell me make an Ar - gen-tine Rose! I need to be thrill-ing, and I shall be

Rain - bow High! They must have ex - cite-ment, and so must
Rain - bow High! They need their es - cape, and so do

Don't Cry For Me Argentina

Music by Andrew Lloyd Webber
Lyrics by Tim Rice

out of the win-dow, stay-ing out of the sun. So I chose free - dom

Run-ning a-round try-ing ev-'ry-thing new, but no-thing im-pressed me at all, I

nev-er ex-pect-ed it to. Don't cry for me Ar-gen - ti - na _____ the

truth is I nev - er left you: All through my wild days, my mad ex - ist-ence, I kept my

ANOTHER SUITCASE IN ANOTHER HALL

MUSIC BY ANDREW LLOYD WEBBER
LYRICS BY TIM RICE

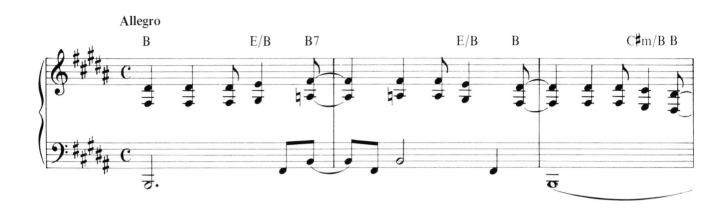

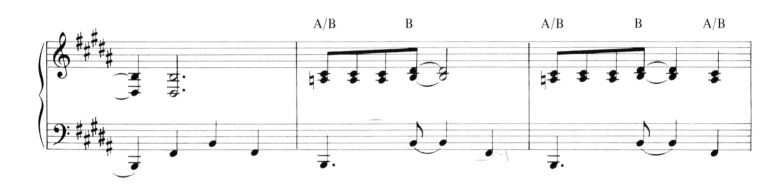

I don't ex-pect __ my
Time and time __ a -
Call in three __ months'

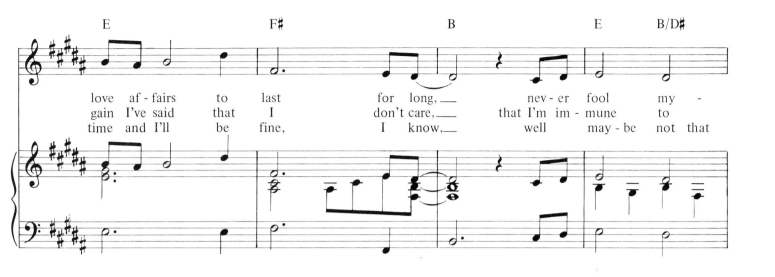

love af - fairs to last for long, __ nev - er fool my -
gain I've said that I don't care, __ that I'm im - mune to
time and I'll be fine, I know, __ well may - be not that

self that my dreams __ will come true. Be - ing used_ to
gloom, that I'm hard ___ through and through. But ev - 'ry time_ it
fine but I'll sur - vive ___ an - y - how. I won't re - call __ the

trou - ble, I __ an - ti - ci - pate __ it, but all the same I
mat - ters all __ my words de - sert __ me, so an - y - one can
names and pla - ces of this sad oc - ca - sion, but that's no con - so -

hate it,
hurt me,
la - tion,

would - n't you?
and they do.
here and now.

So what hap-pens

now? So what hap-pens now?

CHOIR

An - oth - er suit-case in an - oth - er hall, take your pic-ture off an -

oth - er wall, you'll get by, you al - ways have be - fore,

50

High Flying Adored

Music by Andrew Lloyd Webber
Lyrics by Tim Rice

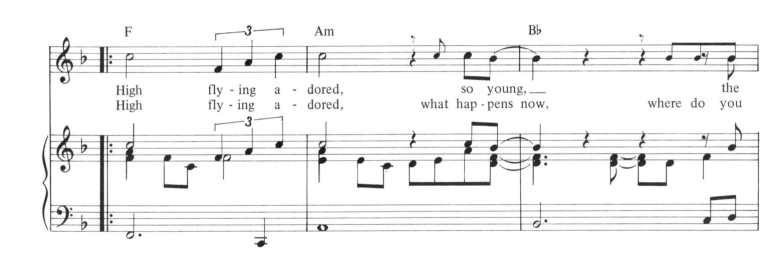

High fly - ing a - dored, so young, the
High fly - ing a - dored, what hap - pens now, where do you

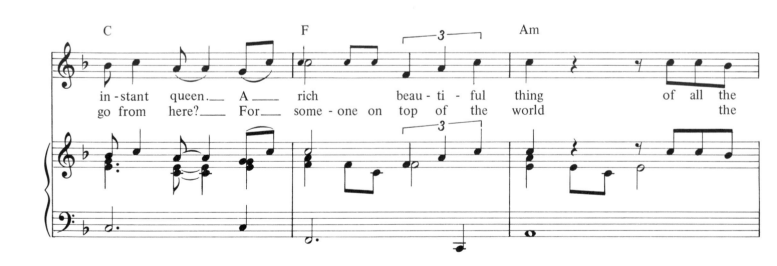

in - stant queen.__ A __ rich beau - ti - ful thing of all the
go from here?__ For__ some - one on top of the world the

High fly - ing _ a -
dored, I've been called names, but they're the stran - gest.
My sto - ry's quite us - u - al, lo - cal girl makes
good, weds fa - mous man, _ I was slap in the right _

CATS

Memory

Music by Andrew Lloyd Webber
Text by Trevor Nunn after T.S. Eliot

Day - light.___ I must wait for the sun - rise,___ I must think of a new life ___ And I must-n't give in._____ When the dawn comes to-night will be a me-mo-ry too ___ And a new day ___ will be - gin.

Mr. Mistoffelees

Music by Andrew Lloyd Webber
Text by T.S. Eliot

look for a knife or a fork
in from the gar - den for hours,
And you think it is mere - ly mis-placed,
While he was a-sleep in the hall.
You have
And

seen it one mo - ment, and then it is gawn! But you'll find it next week ly - ing out on the lawn.
not long a - go ___ this phe-no-me-nal cat ___ Pro-duced se - ven kit - tens right out of a hat! ___

To Coda ⊕

D.S. al Coda

And we all say:
And we all said:

⊕ *CODA* CHORUS

F   C/E   Gm7   C7

Oh! Well I ne-ver! Was_there e - ver a cat so cle-ver as

F   F/A   Bb | **1.** *Repeat ad lib.* | **Last time**   Dm

Ma - gi -cal Mis - ter Mis-tof - fel -ees!   fel -ees!

SOLO

Ladies and gentlemen, I give
you the marvellous, Magical
Mister Mistoffelees! Presto!

68

GUS THE THEATRE CAT

Music by Andrew Lloyd Webber
Text by T.S. Eliot

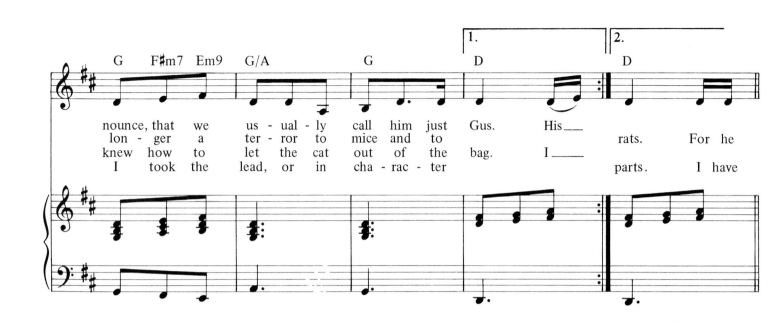

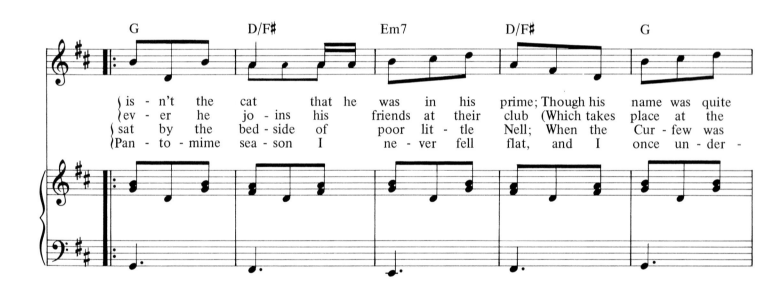

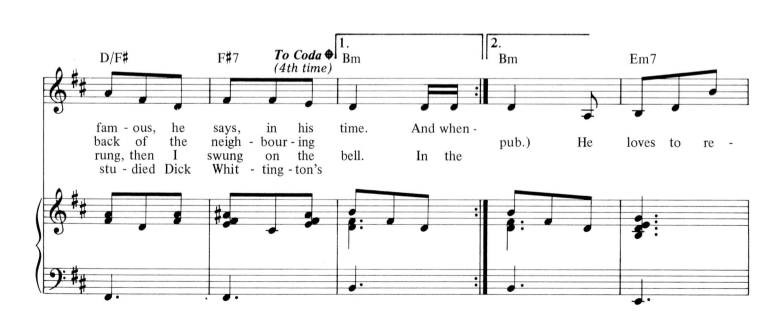

gale them, if some-one else pays, With an-ec-dotes drawn from his palm-i-est days. For he once was a Star of the high-est de-gree: He has act-ed with / likes to re-late his suc-cess on the Halls, Where the Gal-le-ry

1. Irv-ing, he's act-ed with Tree. And he
once gave him sev-en cat - calls. But his grand-est cre - a-tion, as

he loves to tell, Was Fire - frore - fid - dle, the Fiend of the Fell.

72

for-mance he once walked on pat, when some ac - tor sug - ges -ted the need for a cat. And I

say: Now, these kit - tens, they do not get trained As we did in the
nev - er get drilled in a re - gu - lar troupe, And they think they are

days when Vic - tor - i - a reigned. They
smart, just to jump through a hoop. And he says as he scratch - es him -

self with his claws: Well, the Thea - tre is cer - tain - ly not what it was. These

mod-ern pro-duc-tions are all ve-ry well, but there's no-thing to e-qual, from

what I hear tell. That mo-ment of mys-te-ry When I made his-to-ry As

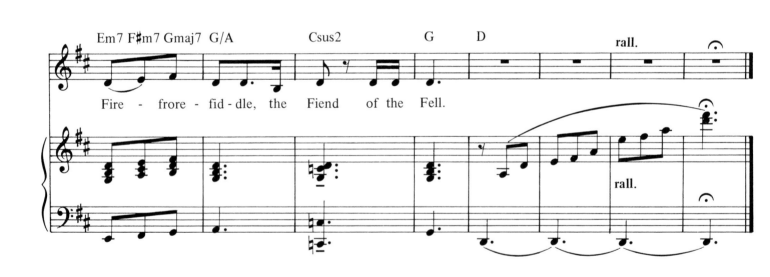

Fire - frore - fid-dle, the Fiend of the Fell.

GUS *(Sung reprise)*

And I once crossed the stage on a telegraph wire,
To rescue a child when a house was on fire.
And I think that I still can much better than most,
Produce blood-curdling noises to bring on the Ghost.
I once played Growltiger, could do it again . . .

SONG AND DANCE

Tell Me On A Sunday

Music by Andrew Lloyd Webber
Lyrics by Don Black

Don't write a let-ter when you want to leave,

Don't call me at 3 a.m. from a friend's a-part-ment; I'd like to choose How I

spend the day; Take me to a zoo that's got chim-pan-zees, __ Tell me

poco animato

on a Sun - day please. Don't want to know who's to blame,

It won't help know-ing. Don't want to fight day and night, bad e-nough you're go-ing.

rallentando

R.H.

Don't leave in si - lence with no words at all.

Don't get drunk and slam the door;— That's no way to end this; I know how I ____ want you to say good-bye; Find a cir-cus ring with a fly-ing tra-peze,— Tell me on a Sun-day please. I don't want to fight day and night; bad e-nough you're go-ing. Don't leave in si-lence

UNEXPECTED SONG

MUSIC BY ANDREW LLOYD WEBBER
LYRICS BY DON BLACK

I have ne - ver felt like this, for once I'm lost for
I don't know what's go - ing on can't work it out at

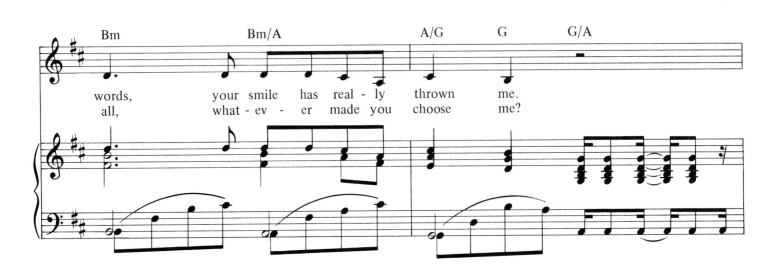

words, your smile has real - ly thrown me.
all, what - ev - er made you choose me?

2.

D   G   Am/G   D/G

hear - ing.   I   have ne - ver felt like   this,   for once I'm lost for

cresc.   f   a tempo

Em   Em/D   D/C   C   C/D   G

words,   your smile has real - ly thrown   me.   This   is   not like me at

Am/G   D/G   Em   Em/D   D/C   C   C/D

all,   I ne - ver thought I'd know   the kind of love you've shown   me.

G   G7   C

Now,   no mat - ter where I   am   no mat - ter what I   do,   I   see your face ap -

Take That Look Off Your Face

Music by Andrew Lloyd Webber
Lyrics by Don Black

hate it   when he's a - way. __   2. You

know   if he had-n't gone__
on- ly   a wo - man   can__

CHORUS   (Backing Vocals)

Take that   look off your face__ (Take that look off your face__) I can
No I   did - n't dig deep_ (No I   did - n't dig deep_) I did

see through your smile__   (I can   see through your smile __) You would
not want to know__   (I did   not want to know__) Well you

love to be right,__   I bet   you did-n't   sleep good last night,__ could-n't
don't in - ter - fere__ when you're scared of the   things you might hear __ when he's

89

The Last Man In My Life

Music by Andrew Lloyd Webber
Lyrics by Don Black

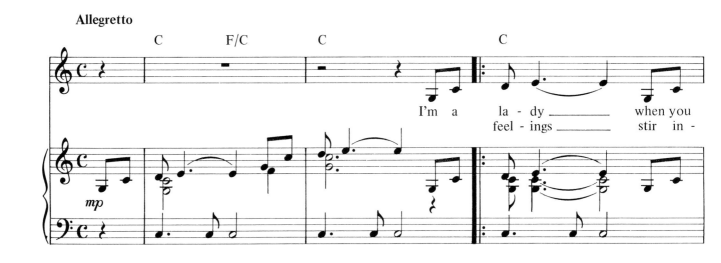

morn -ing,_____ I am cer -tain _____ you're the last man in my life. _____

I'm a la -dy_____ when you kiss me,_____ I'm a
feel -ings_____ stir in - side me,_____ used to

child when you are leav - ing, _____ I'm a wo - man _____ ev - 'ry
think nights were for sleep - ing, _____ be - ing want - ed _____ is a

time our bo - dies meet _____ com - plete. Long lost
thrill I nev - er knew _____ till you.

Now I'm a - live, in - side I'm glow - ing, I'm how I want to

be, lov - ing you I can be me, just me. It's the

REQUIEM

Pie Jesu

Music by Andrew Lloyd Webber

re-qui-em.

SOLO BOY *mp*

Pi - e Je - su,_____ pi - e Je - su,_____ pi - e

Ab   Bbm/Ab   Eb7/Ab   Ab

Qui tol - lis pec-ca-ta mun-di,

Je - su,_____ pi - e Je - su, Qui tol - lis pec-ca-ta mun-di,

SOPRANO

p

ALTO

*Hm*_____

TENOR

BASS

p

Bbm7/Db   Eb7   Db   Eb

101

STARLIGHT EXPRESS

There's Me

Music by Andrew Lloyd Webber
Lyrics by Richard Stilgoe

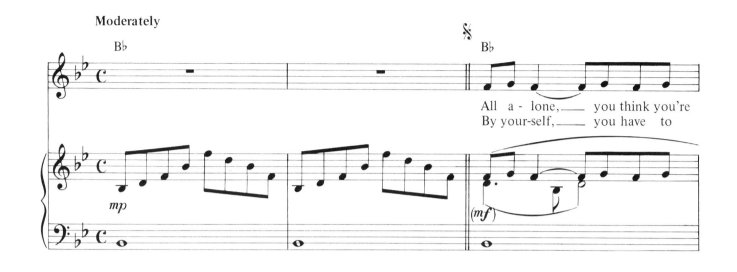

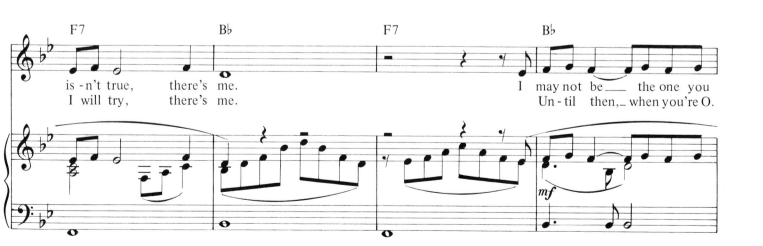

107

Starlight Express

Music by Andrew Lloyd Webber
Lyrics by Richard Stilgoe

Moderately

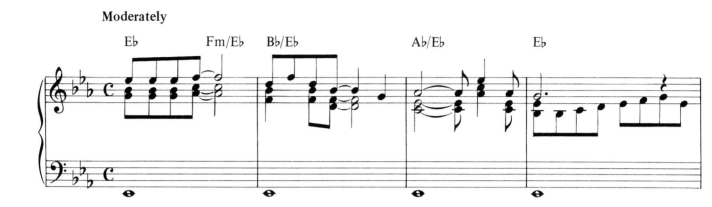

When your good - nights have been said ___ and you are
take me a - way ___ but bring me

ly - ing in bed ___ with the cov - ers pulled ___ up tight; ___ and though you
back be - fore day - light, and in the time ___ be - tween ___ take me to

Star- light Ex - press,___ ans - wer me yes,___ I

don't want you ___ to go.___ Star - light Ex - press,___

you must con - fess___ are you real,___ yes or no?

Star-light Ex - press,___ ans - wer me yes, ___ I don't want you ___ to go.

rall.

111

Only You

Music by Andrew Lloyd Webber
Lyrics by Richard Stilgoe

113

Make Up My Heart

Music by Andrew Lloyd Webber
Lyrics by Richard Stilgoe

Moderately

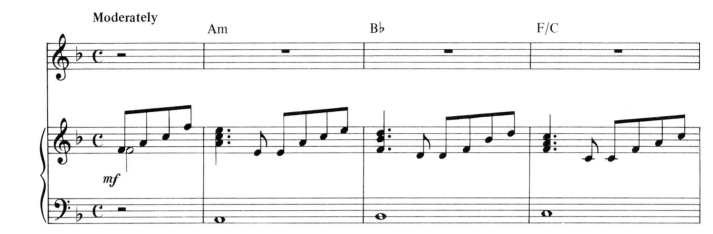

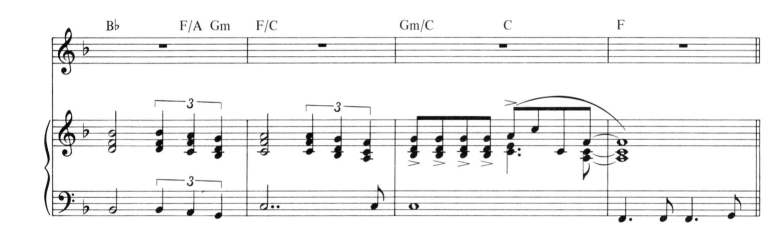

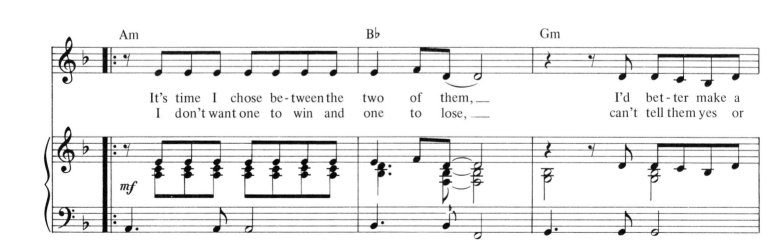

It's time I chose be-tween the two of them, ___ I'd bet-ter make a
I don't want one to win and one to lose, ___ can't tell them yes or

D.$. al Coda   ⊕ CODA

heart. One can make me

laugh, one can make me sigh, why tear my-self in half, so who gets the

part, make up my heart.

PHANTOM OF THE OPERA

All I Ask Of You

Music by Andrew Lloyd Webber
Lyrics by Charles Hart
Additional lyrics by Richard Stilgoe

124

Music Of The Night

Music by Andrew Lloyd Webber
Lyrics by Charles Hart
Additional lyrics by Richard Stilgoe

Andante

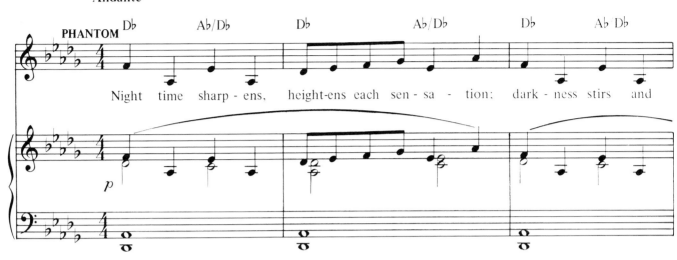

Night time sharp-ens, height-ens each sen-sa-tion; dark-ness stirs and

wakes im-ag-in-a-tion. Si-lent-ly the sen-ses a-ban-don their de-fen-ces.

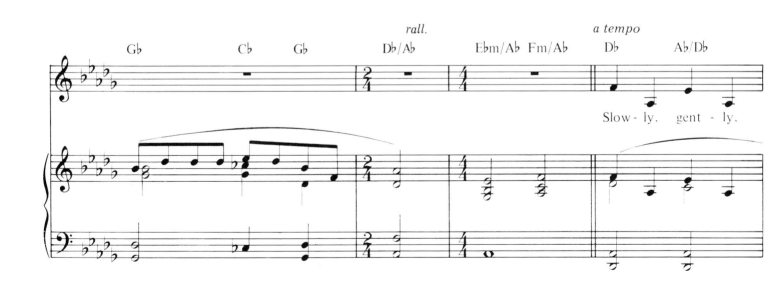

Slow-ly, gent-ly,

130

Wishing You Were Somehow Here Again

Music by Andrew Lloyd Webber
Lyrics by Charles Hart
Additional Lyrics by Richard Stilgoe

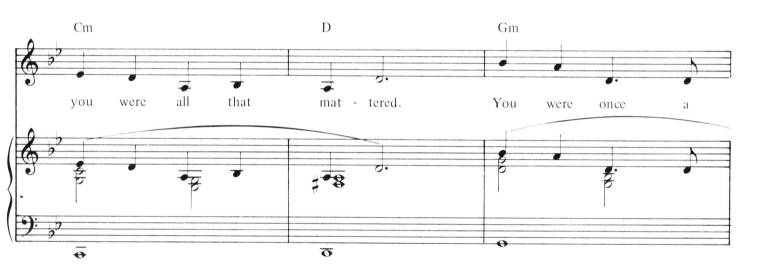

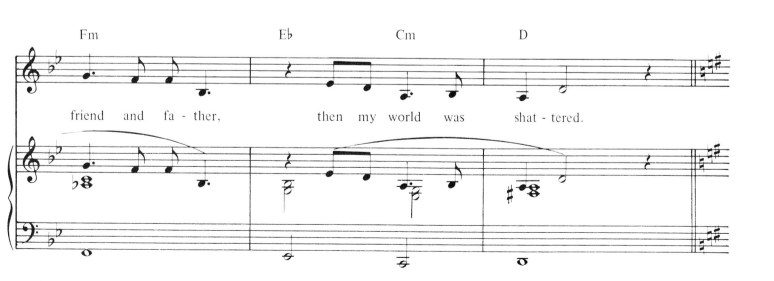

dream-ing of you won't help me to do all that you dreamed I

poco meno mosso

could. Pass - ing bells and sculp - ted an-gels,

cold and mon - u - men - tal, seem for you the

rit.

wrong com-pan-ions; you were warm and gen - tle.

bye. Try to for - give, teach me to live.
give me the strength to try. No more me - mor-ies, no more
si - lent tears, no more gaz-ing a - cross the wast - ed years. Help me
say good - bye! Help me say good - bye!

THE PHANTOM OF THE OPERA

MUSIC BY ANDREW LLOYD WEBBER
LYRICS BY CHARLES HART
ADDITIONAL LYRICS BY RICHARD STILGOE & MIKE BATT

Allegro—vivace

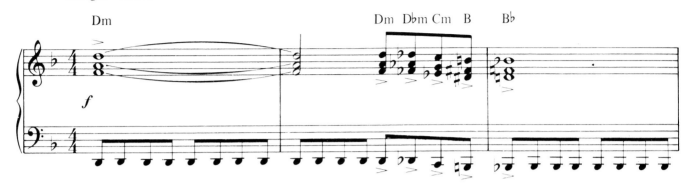

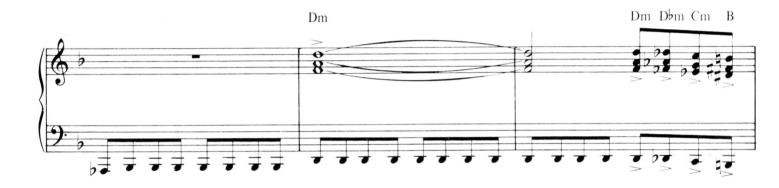

In sleep he sang to me, _____ in dreams he came,

137

141

142

143

Exclusive Distributors:
Music Sales Limited,
8/9 Frith Street, London, W1V 5TZ, England.
Music Sales Pty. Limited,
120 Rothschild Avenue, Rosebery, NSW 2018, Australia.

This Edition © Copyright 1987 published by The Really Useful Group plc
by kind permission of the copyright owners.

ISBN 0-7119-1203-3
ORDER NO. RG10054

Book Designed by
Pearce Marchbank Studio

Music Edited and Arranged by
Roger Day

Music Engraving by Music Print Limited

Joseph And The Amazing Technicolor® Dreamcoat photograph reproduced
by kind permission of David Land and Superstar Ventures Limited
Jesus Christ Superstar photograph by Laurie Asprey
Evita photograph by Zoë Dominic
Cats photograph by John Haynes
Song And Dance photographs by Nobby Clark
Requiem photographs by Clive Barda
Starlight Express photograph by Nobby Clark
Phantom Of The Opera photograph by Clive Barda

Printed In Scotland By
Scotprint Limited, Musselburgh.